UNLIKELY HEROES

The Story Of An Agrarian Renaissance

Photographs and Text by
Walter Lewis

Foreword by
Colin Tudge

Essay by
Stephen Devlin

Walter
Lewis

Introduction

When a food production system is as broke as the one of the western world is, it is no good tinkering around the edges. The current system is destroying the very earth on which we depend and yet, in its drive to cheaper and cheaper food, is producing more and more imbalance between the 'haves' and 'have nots'. A radical new approach – or approaches – is required. It is not a question of going back to anywhere, rather a case of learning from the past and moving on with farming and growing systems which are actively regenerative of farms and the soil, the environment and communities, and, ultimately, our individual souls.

I am a documentary photographer who, in 2015, travelled around England and Wales seeking out people who have a made choice to produce food in an alternative way. In such cases, production is more often than not locally-focused, often community-based, organic or biodynamic in method, small in scale, highly rotational and highly mixed, low in energy use, low in intervention yet high in animal welfare. It is everything that factory farming is not, and produces food of quality and seasonality within, or close to, consuming communities.

In choosing to grow in this way the practitioners are not opting for an easy way out. The life is demanding, and motivation is often linked to environmental activism. Practising a new agroecology can be as much political statement as it is business. In choosing such a way of life, these farmers and growers provide the rest of us with a choice as to where we source our daily food. Is it to be sustainably sourced or are we to support the fault-bestrewn *status quo* as found in every supermarket? It is a choice which, through its availability, fundamentally tests our mindset towards the earth on which we ultimately depend.

Barbara Beveridge is proprietor of **Seasonal Salads** just outside of Stokesley in North Yorkshire. She leases just a fifth of an acre of land from a local farmer on which she produces exquisite micro-salads. With the help of her polytunnel she manages to produce all year round. With much of her production generated by natural seeding, harvesting is as much a foraging operation as farming with each salad a unique mix.

Ahimsa Dairy Foundation is a demonstrator of slaughter-free dairy farming which was set up by Nicola Pazdzierska and Sanjay Tanna. Their mission is to make slaughter-free milk a reality across the UK. Calves have access to their mothers for at least six months, and no cow, calf or bull is ever killed, with all allowed to live out their lives to their natural span - an extraordinarily ambitious project. Based on a site just north of Leicester, the girls bit currently produces around 23,000 of litres of milk a year, with the milk available through a membership scheme, whilst the boys are being trained as working oxen. Whilst the milking herd was initially in Kent, the rest of the herd was looked after in Leicestershire by **Govinda Das**, a herdsman who moved to the UK from Hungary where he ran a slaughter-free dairy herd!

Colin Tudge

Foreword

If we, the human species and our fellow creatures, are to come through the next few centuries in a tolerable state then we need to re-think *everything* from first principles – politics, economics, science, morality – which means that we need to bring about an across-the-board renaissance; a re-birth. But of course, too, most importantly, we need to *act* appropriately: to shape everything that we do from education to the provision of energy in ways that are truly beneficial to people, and respectful to the biosphere at large, not just for now but in the long haul – meaning the next million years and then some. Above all, and most urgently, we need a complete re-think and re-structuring of farming and food culture: the 'Agrarian Renaissance' that is the subject of this book.

It's all too obvious, though, that the people with the most power in the world – the oligarchy of governments, corporates, banks, and their attendant experts and intellectuals – are not going to change their ways. They seem to take it almost to be self-evident that the present *modus operandi* is what's needed – industrialized farming (and industrialized everything else) within the ultra-competitive neoliberal economy; that the *status quo* is the best that can be done even though one in seven people go hungry, while half our fellow species are threatened with imminent extinction, and global warming is already with us. Besides, the implication is, the blame for all that's wrong rests with humanity itself. So, if

the Agrarian Renaissance is to happen then it has to be brought about by people like us, people-at-large. 'Ordinary Joes' - a derogatory soubriquet that should be a badge of honour like 'Desert Rat' or 'Suffragette'.

This Agrarian Renaissance has already begun. Many millions, probably billions, of people in the non-industrialised ('undeveloped') world continue farming and cooking in ways that could ensure that we are all well fed without wrecking the rest of the world. Millions more (though that's a guess) within the industrialised ('developed') world have now also broken from the mainstream and are exploring ways of growing, marketing, and preparing food that could keep us and the planet in good heart even at this late hour. Such agriculture - that really could feed us all well - is rooted in tradition: low-input (primarily organic) farms, as mixed as possible, intricately managed by plenty of skilled farmers and growers, and generally small to medium sized. Such agriculture provides 70 per cent of the world's food, and with a little help – mainly logistic, in part economic, and sometimes technical – could easily support us all and still be wildlife-friendly. Yet, such farming is horribly under-supported and much derided in high places. In absolute contrast, the industrialized farming that now attracts more than 90% of funding and research is based on high-input, high-tech, minimum or zero labour monocultures run on the largest possible scale. These industrialized factories and plantations do immense damage to

societies and to the biosphere – indeed are one of the prime causes of the world's current ills – and yet they provide only 30% of the world's food.

So the traditional farmers, and those who now seek to emulate their ways, must swim against the political and economic tide, and for the most part are seriously under-rewarded - indeed include some of the world's poorest people. Yet they, at the very least, are building and keeping afloat the life-rafts that all of us will need if industrial farming continues on its present course. With luck and a following wind, pioneer enterprises though will multiply and coalesce to form a new food network the world over. A new food network which will evolve to meet the needs both of humanity and of the biosphere. It will not, as is the case with industrial farming, be imposed from on high and designed primarily to generate wealth that stays in the hands of the dominant minority.

Far from the public eye, these small farmers, traditionalist yet pioneering, are the world's true heroes. Walter Lewis does us all a great service by bringing them, and their endeavours, to our attention in these excellent portraits. They are the 'Seeds of the Renaissance'.

Colin Tudge is author of 'Six Steps Back to the Land' and founder of the College for Real Farming and Food Culture (http://collegeforrealfarming.org/).

Chris Walsh and *Helen Woodcock* are the founders of *Kindling Trust*, a Manchester-based charity working with communities, farmers, practitioners, activists, and policy makers to create and support progressive food projects around the city. Central to their efforts is a starter farm on which quarter acre plots are leased to would-be farmers so that they can begin to build such a life, and these emergent farmers are supported by training courses and by the Kindling Trust's Land Army, a team of keen voluntary workers. The ultimate aim is to engage the support of the major public and private sector food buyers across the city to establish a large farm plus social change centre for Greater Manchester, and incorporating workers' 'Ecommodation'.

Stephen Devlin

Closing the distance

If there is one word to describe the novelty of the contemporary food system it is 'distance'. In so many ways the people that eat the food have become distant from the people that grow it. There is distance covered by grain, fuel and migrant workers in the global market for production inputs; the distance that final products travel in planes, ships and lorries to reach market; people living in urban communities ever more distant from the source of their sustenance; and, perhaps most importantly, the psychological distance between consumers and the reality of modern food production which is the essential ingredient to keep it all going.

As the decades have passed, we have seen not just profound economic and social change, but also significant changes in personal identity and psychology. In particular, for the last few decades, the neoliberal revolution has made deliberate changes not only to economic relationships – privatising, liberalising, deregulating – but also to the way that people see themselves, their relations to one another and to the economy. In the food system, as in so many other areas, we have learned to think of our identity first and foremost as consumers. We treat food as if it were any other commodity, purchased and traded in anonymous markets. Sovereign consumers, acting as individuals, supposedly guide the market through their carefully calculated choices, and suppliers merely compete to provide the highest value service. Through the daily practice of a market economy our

identities have shifted from collective to primarily individual. Yet since the food system and all it entails, from health to environment, is unalterably a collective endeavour, this individualised identity alienates us from it.

Below I review some of the things in which the neoliberal food system, and the distance it creates between individuals and the collective, is failing.

Breaking the Planet

The multi-dimensional distance that characterises our food system allows environmental problems to be systematically ignored because they are inconspicuous to the majority. The degradation of soils and precipitous decline of farmland birds are tragedies that have practically no perceivable relevance for most in modern society. Even among informed technocrats the environmental consequences of the modern food system seem to get side-lined. At the 2015 Paris climate talks energy and transport systems took centre stage and agriculture was a footnote, despite the sector accounting for nearly a quarter of global greenhouse gas emissions.[1] In the UK, around a sixth of our total emissions are in some way related to food, whether that's through production, manufacturing, distribution, or household food waste.[2] Policy experts have churned out an infinite number of research papers and advocacy strategies for an energy transition – where is the equivalent

research effort for agriculture? We cannot prevent the brutal impacts of climate change without a livelier debate about alternative agricultural models.

Even if you put climate change to one side, there are direct and immediate consequences of the way we produce food in the UK. Agriculture and food manufacturing are major sources of air and water pollutants, with public health and ecological costs in the form of cancers, respiratory disease and eutrophication of rivers and other waterways.[3] Economists refer to these costs as "externalities", which makes them sound abstract, but we mustn't forget that these are costs that we all pay every day through our contribution to health care and cleaning up pollution. They're not in your mind as you checkout at the supermarket, but they are no less real in terms of impact on your finances.

On the other hand, some environmental problems do hit the supermarket till, and nothing more so than waste. A family with children spends around £700 each year on food that they end up putting in the bin, eventually decomposing into greenhouse gases.[4] Millions of tonnes of edible food, grown using precious land and resources, go immediately back into the ground having served no useful purpose. Nobody gains from such a situation except supermarkets selling BOGOF deals and multi-pack vegetables and, of course, waste management companies. And it's not just money and resources that the food system wastes, it is also extremely wasteful of energy. With very high energy inputs from fossil fuels and machinery, and low energy conversion rates because of our relatively high consumption of meat (where most of the energy from plants gets lost), the thermodynamic efficiency of our food system could be drastically improved. Rough calculations indicate that for every eight units of energy that we put into our food system we get only one unit back from the food we eat.[2]

The scale of the environmental challenges is huge, but the planetary consequences of food tend to be ignored as for most of us the only connection to it is the eating of it. We do not feel the environmental effect as we bite into a sandwich, especially if we have no idea where it came from or how it was made The enormous structural shift of economic activity away from the land and towards service industries has physically and psychologically separated us from where our food comes from and created an industry composed of large and labour-free farms producing only a small number of uniform commodities. This has been necessary, many argue, to exploit economies of scale and keep food prices low for the benefit of the poorest. Nonetheless, as an expert report concluded: *'Many of the problems in food systems are linked specifically to the uniformity at the heart of industrial agriculture, and its reliance on chemical fertilisers and pesticides.'*[5] In other words, economic logic does not necessarily entail environmental logic. This isn't a necessary trade off, but neither is it a natural complementarity.

How, then, do we close the distance between environmental consequences and the production and consumption decisions that lead to them? Many advocate for demand-side responses, whether through labelling products differently and imploring consumers to make ethical choices, or, by financial incentives to guide those decisions. *Unlikely Heroes* highlights solutions that come from the other side – producers taking things into their own hands and producing food that doesn't create "externalities" despite the absence of any policy that would reward them for it. These people are environmental pioneers and the most important way to reward them is by updating policy frameworks that lag behind. A simplistic interpretation of economics will have you to believe that change is driven by consumer preferences and that government can, at best, only guide those preferences through appropriate financial incentives. In the real world, however, consumers are more followers than leaders, their preferences being shaped by government and businesses. Given the scale and urgency of environmental problems, we have no choice but to foster a farming system that works for the planet, and lead consumers along that journey.

A Broken Economic Model

When a system is dysfunctional it pays to ask: Who actually benefits from the way this works? As we've seen, the environment is a clear victim of our food system and yet the taxpayer also forks out billions each year to subsidise farms. Yet despite huge state support many farms are still unprofitable or barely profitable, and farmers typically live under conditions of insecurity and economic pressure from supply chains, and the same time the problem of food poverty remains desperate in spite of historically low food prices. So there is no shortage of disgruntled stakeholders in the food system. How can this system work so badly for so many?

As with so many sectors, the problem lies with the concentration of economic and political power in a small number of hands, leaving the majority disenfranchised and exploited. This is visible in the increasing concentration of land among a small number of wealthy owners that drives the price upwards – all of the UK's agricultural land is held by just 0.25% of its population and the price of an acre has more than trebled over the last decade.[2] It's visible in the abusive behaviour of supermarkets with enormous buying power that force their suppliers to bear the cost of waste and sudden changes to orders – the UK's Groceries Code Adjudicator recently lambasted Tesco for effectively extorting suppliers out of millions of pounds.[6] You can see it also in the lack of representation for small-scale producers in mainstream bodies and their ineligibility for the subsidies that larger producers receive. The discipline of economics has surprisingly little to say about power, yet it is the distribution and exercise of power more than anything that drives the perverse economics of the food system.

But beyond the current market structures there are longer-term socio-economic forces at work. There is a self-reinforcing dynamic between poverty, cheap food and environmental damage that we have to escape. Poor workers can only afford to eat if the price of food is low, so industrialists can only avoid increasing wages if they can force the price of food down (hence the repeal of the Corn Laws). But keeping food prices down requires economising on the factors that go into its production – substituting expensive workers for machines and fossil fuels, exploiting economies of scale through larger farms, neglecting more laborious methods that prevent environmental damage, and keeping wages low throughout the supply chain. That creates environmental problems but also, since 11% of our workforce is employed in the food system,[2] reinforces the poverty that started the cycle. The individual problems of the food system cannot be solved in isolation, nor can they be treated as separate from the wider economy. More prosperous workers and a sustainable food system should go hand in hand.

On current trends, however, agricultural workers may eventually disappear altogether. A new wave of automated and robotic agri-technology (championed and funded by the government) is expected to dramatically change the way we produce. The impact on the environment is ambiguous: better technological could use resources more sparingly, but may also encourage further monoculture, for example. But the implication for workers is clear: there will be fewer. For many this is progress: workers are "released" to produce more economically valuable goods and ever fewer back-breaking jobs need doing. Indeed, we should not romanticise work that is genuinely unpleasant, and it seems to be true that the UK public have a grim view of farming as a potential career. Nonetheless, the fact that similar trends will sweep across most economic sectors leaves the question of how the "released" workers will secure their livelihood as unanswered. Moreover, many of the reasons for the poor quality of many jobs in food and farming, from low pay to insecurity, are socially constructed and not related to the inherent nature of the work.

Breaking Communities

As always, environmental and economic problems are inseparable from social problems. In the case of our food system an epidemic of diet-related ill health is currently debilitating communities, exacerbating inequalities and straining public services. In recent decades obesity rates have increased rapidly and the growth in diabetes cases is deeply worrying. The cost to our health service alone (not to mention to the rest of our economy) is measured in billions.[7] What's worse is that we increasingly understand that health problems are not uniformly spread across the population but rather they are frequently associated with economic deprivation.[8] It's clear that a "cheap food" policy may have prevented the worst ravages of undernourishment, but new problems of malnourishment have been created.

Neither have we even managed to eliminate hunger itself. Despite spending the lowest proportion of national income on food in the EU[2], we in the UK still see food banks surfacing to support people in periods of desperate need. It's clear that no matter how cheap food is, in the absence of a guarantee to meet people's basic needs, there will always be hunger. The existence of food banks in such numbers is a blot on our conscience – it is difficult to read the testimonies of food bank users and not to feel a deep sense of shame at the despair and stigma they experience. This type of relationship with the food system will never prioritise sustainability or even healthfulness. Again, we see that a sustainable food system and the elimination of poverty must go hand in hand.

Another consequence of the current food system is more difficult to pin down. "Food culture", the set of social phenomena that affect how and what we eat, and how we interpret what it means with respect to our place in society, is in constant flux. But that does not mean that we shouldn't debate and analyse how it is changing and how that affects us.

Undoubtedly, the culture surrounding food affects our health and well-being. To take one small example, the idea of a meal has changed drastically over time. Data shows that instead of three distinct times of day during which most people were eating 50 years ago, now we eat at all times of day with much less distinct peak times.[9] Many of us eat on the go, in front of the television or alone. The evidence is thin, but there is at least some suggestion that shared family meals are beneficial for child development, reducing behavioural problems and increasing performance at school.[2] We might extend the concept of food culture to include, for example, social norms around body image and dieting, attitudes to waste, or various fashions driven by celebrity chefs and bloggers. Although it is ambiguous in definition, culture change creates problems but is also a critical part of the solution. As Margaret Thatcher famously understood, neoliberalism was as much about changing hearts and minds as it was about changing policy. A counter-revolution in food culture must surely be necessary. In many ways, the people in *Unlikely Heroes* have undertaken this revolution for themselves; the job that remains is to bring it to society at large.

Reclaiming the Collective

This has been a pessimistic assessment of our food system and it's right to be highly conscious of the scale and urgency of the problems. Nonetheless, there are reasons for optimism. Indeed, *Unlikely Heroes* provides us with many. The key, for me, is to appreciate the interconnection between the problems that we crudely categorise as environmental, economic or social. Economics drives the how we treat the environment; the environment affects the health and resilience of our society; the vigour of our communities underpins the functioning of our economy. That's why it's so encouraging to see that for so many of those in *Unlikely Heroes* it's not just about food, narrowly defined, but also about employment, skills, mental health, or community. The people of *Unlikely Heroes* close the gap between how we think about a multitude of societal problems and they close the distance between growers and eaters, in geography and psychology. But also they demonstrate a conscious change in identity with respect to the food system – they emphasise collaboration, not competition, and they do not hide from the inherently social nature of producing and consuming food. *Unlikely Heroes* help us to reflect on our own identities as consumers or producers and help us to close some of this distance.

Stephen Devlin is a senior economist at the New Economics Foundation (http://neweconomics.org) where he provides commentary and analysis on a range of environmental and economic policy areas. He previously worked as an economist in the Department for Environment, Food and Agriculture.

References

1. Smith, P. et al. *Agriculture, Forestry and Other Land Use (AFOLU)* in 'Climate Change 2014: Mitigation of Climate Change. Contribution of Working Group III to the Fifth Assessment Report of the Intergovernmental Panel on Climate Change' (Edenhofer, O. et al. eds.) pp 811–922 (Cambridge University Press, 2014) See http://www.ipcc.ch/pdf/assessment-report/ar5/wg3/ipcc_wg3_ar5_chapter11.pdf

2. Devlin, S. et al. *Urgent Recall: Our Food System Under Review* (New Economics Foundation, 2014) See http://b.3cdn.net/nefoundation/1bfd1f66401d3b5f4b_fsm6vjoti.pdf

3. Pretty, J. N. et al. *An assessment of the total external costs of UK agriculture* Agric. Syst. 65, pp 113–136 (2000).

4. Love Food Hate Waste Website: *The Facts about Food Waste* (Waste and Resources Action Programme) See http://www.lovefoodhatewaste.com/node/2472

5. Jacobs, N. (ed) *From Uniformity to Diversity: A Paradigm Shift from Industrial Agriculture to Diversified Agroecological Systems.* (International Panel of Experts on Food Systems, 2016) See http://www.ipes-food.org/images/Reports/UniformityToDiversity_FullReport.pdf

6. Crown Copyright Report: *Investigation into Tesco plc.* (Groceries Code Adjudicator, 2016) See https://www.gov.uk/government/uploads/system/uploads/attachment_data/file/494840/GCA_Tesco_plc_final_report_26012016_-_version_for_download.pdf

7. Crown Copyright Report: *The Economic Burden of Obesity* (National Obesity Observatory, 2010) See http://www.noo.org.uk/uploads/doc/vid_8575_Burdenofobesity151110MG.pdf

8. Crown Copyright Report: *Adult Obesity and Type 2 Diabetes* (Public Health England, 2014) See https://www.gov.uk/government/uploads/system/uploads/attachment_data/file/338934/Adult_obesity_and_type_2_diabetes_.pdf

9. Discussion Paper: *Food: An Analysis of the Issues.* (Cabinet Office, 2008) See http://webarchive.nationalarchives.gov.uk/+/http:/www.cabinetoffice.gov.uk/media/cabinetoffice/strategy/assets/food/food_analysis.pdf

Waiting.
Contemplating.
Filling in.
Slow days
Born out of long nights.
Restless for new life,
Tentative in belief.

Tasha Stephens lives and works with husband, Patch, at ***Little Brympton Ecological Micro-Farm*** just outside Chiselborough in Somerset. Little Brympton owner, Albert Holman, had run a market garden and sold cut flowers from there for 30 years, but had to move out due to ill health. Finding Tasha and Patch with a vision closely aligned to his own, Albert welcomed them as tenants of his 2 acre garden with its one-room off-grid wooden farmhouse. From their newly self-built shop, Tasha and Patch now sell home-grown seasonal veg, salad mixes and cut flowers, wild mushrooms, home-made preserves, honey from their own bees and their speciality, sea buckthorn juice made from wild Somerset berries.

Neil Marshall is a co-founder of **Growing with Grace** near Settle in North Yorkshire. The business, set up as a co-operative and social enterprise with financial surpluses reinvested back into the business or to community dividends, is located on around 2 acres of land alongside the very busy A65. Almost all of land is under glass, the site having previously been a plant nursery. Now this glass cover enables organic vegetables and salads to be produced year round and supplied through a weekly and organic home-delivery programme and the on-site shop.

Stuart Jones is one of three people who set up **Moss Brook Grower**s, an organic workers co-operative leasing 21 acres of land from whole-food retail co-operative, Unicorn Grocery, based in Chorlton. The land, just west of Manchester, was purchased by Unicorn in 2008 with the aim of creating a brand new farm through which they could enhance the supply of organic field vegetables and fruit across Manchester and surrounds. Despite many teething problems, long-term faith in the project remains as reflected by the planting of 100's of fruit trees, and the core team working to establish on-site accommodation for at least one grower along with polytunnels which will put the future business on a more financially sound footing.

Tim White lives with his artist partner, Jules, in a small terraced cottage on the main street of Maiden Bradley in Wiltshire and runs 800+ sheep across Wiltshire, Dorset and Devon. He owns no land and is what he calls a 'grazier', basically begging and borrowing access to land, say, from cereal farmers who are leaving a field fallow for a year. None-the-less, the sheep are reared organically and exclusively grass-fed. To support his nomadic business, Tim runs a meticulously documented breeding programme aimed at enhancing low maintenance qualities such as self-shedding fleeces.

Incredible by name, incredible by nature! **Nick Green** created **Incredible Farm** with the aim of teaching small-scale commercial food-growing and marketing skills to young people. The farm is just outside Todmorden. It's a wild and woolly place up amongst the Pennine Hills with its 1 acre of land more moorland bog than fertile plain. Nick planned to ease the burden of the heavy humping work around the site by training his 2 Jersey calves to pull like oxen. At the time of my visit, the cows were winning!

With a backdrop of Pendle Hill and its folklore and history, **Emma O'Reilly** and husband, Ian, are developing **Gazegill Farm** as a business which is fair to the land, respectful of its history, organic in its practices, compassionate to its livestock, and, an integral part of the local community. Their sixty-strong herd of dairy shorthorns is the centrepiece, with the on-site Emma's Dairy processing and selling the milk unpasteurised and unhomogenised. Rare breed pigs, sheep and hens complete the mix, with the meat butchered and sold from the on-site shop.

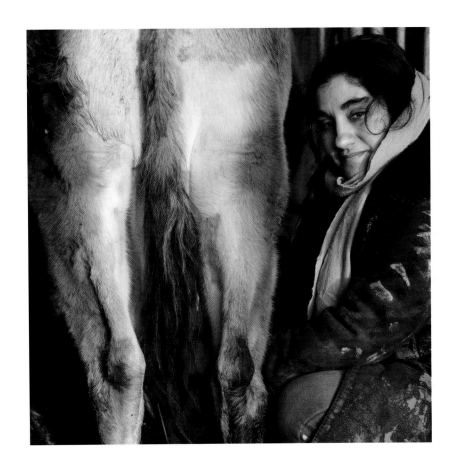

Jyoti Fernades, along with her husband, Dai, and two friends, Kerri and Oli, owns and farms **Five Penny Farm** in Dorset. They all came to Five Penny ten years or so ago when it was around 40 acres of empty fields. Now, it's a highly productive mixed smallholding and the location of 2 self-built wooden family houses with their own solar and wind powered electricity generation, self-contained spring water supply, and 'composting' system for excrement.

Nir Halfon is one of six farmers and growers at **Old Plaw Hatch Farm** near Forest Row in West Sussex. Collectively they constitute a 'on-site' community committed to the principles and practices of thinker and philosopher, Rudolf Steiner, and, in particular, his biodynamic methods which seek to align food growing practice to cosmic energies. The farm comprises a dairy herd, sheep flock, chickens, pigs, a dairy processing unit, and the market garden, co-managed by Nir. The farm produce is predominantly sold through an exceptional farm shop.

Located on 300 acres of open countryside between Leeds and York, **St Helen's Farm** has been in the Watson family for over 100 years. At the turn of the millennium, Jonnie and Fanny Watson took over what had become a pig rearing unit and began its conversion to organic vegetable production. It now grows over 50 varieties of vegetable and salad crops, all of which are certified organic by the Soil Association. Such is the output that on some days Jonnie and the farm crew will pick over a tonne of purple sprouting broccoli - all by hand - to be sold through the farm's sales outlet, **Organic Pantry**, its box scheme and independent retailers across the north of England. Farmhand, **Jamie**, was well into the task the day I visited.

Growing Communities is a community project in Hackney in North London which runs a **Patchwork Farm** within the borough. Patches are small areas of land, often previously brownfield and derelict, which are worked by young self-employed growers in a co-ordinated programme so as to produce the 'Hackney Salad' (pages 92-93) which goes into the Growing Communities' weekly veg bag supplied to around 1000 scheme members. Two of the patches are designated 'market gardens' with employed growers who both produce and provide training to anyone looking to take up a patch. **Sophie** (centre right) and **Paul** (centre left) were such people when I visited, whilst **Sonia and Ida** (left) worked the **Climbing Centre** patch, and Sarah (right) was one of three who worked the **Kynaston Gardens** patch located behind a bank on Stoke Newington High Street.

Oz Austin, and partner, Beth Morgan, have created a business, **Rooting and Fruiting**, based on their passion for fungi and their progressive community and environmental ideals. Their growing facility is high in the hills between Todmorden and Hebden Bridge at Pextenement Farm - an organic dairy farm and itself home of an award-winning cheese. Here, guided by permaculture principles, Oz and Beth target an output beyond the immediate production of their range of mushrooms and spores, aiming that their work inspire and educate so as to improve the well-being of local individuals, community and environment.

Emergent,
Every day a morning.
Dormancy unfolds
Into a theatre of belief.
Endless beginnings.
A bardoic masterpiece.

Wheelbarrow Farm is a mixed smallholding just outside Stroud in Gloucestershire. It's owned by Berni and **Fadia Courts**. Fadia came here many years ago from Palestine. Bernie is a Jew born in Britain. For 20 years Palestinian and Jew have been happily married, building a relationship based on love, compassion and respect. They have also slowly acquired the 10 acres of Wheelbarrow Farm piece by piece and have now decided that it is of sufficient size for them to live there and fully commit to self-sufficiency. A major building programme is underway using low impact straw-bale and wooden construction methods, and the site is being set up independent of mainstream power, water and sanitation.

Just three miles from Exeter, **West Town Farm** is a livestock farm where the land is managed organically, the animals are cared for with respect and compassion and every effort is made to conserve wildlife. The farm is owned by the Church of England and has been leased to the Bragg family for the last three generations. Current tenant, Andy, took over in 1982 and out of concern about animal welfare and farmland biodiversity switched to organic methods, completing conversion in 1992. The beef, lamb, pork and chicken are sold direct from the farm and at local farmers markets. The farm is regularly host to trainees and volunteers such as Norwegian visitor, **Nanna**.

Jo Cartwright has been farming at **Swillington Organic Farm** just on the outskirts of Leeds for well nigh on thirty years. For most of that time, as now, the farm has been home to a range of mainly rare breed cows, pigs, and sheep, all of which are treated with genuine care and compassion. In recent times Jo has also added organic vegetable and salad production to her output with the produce grown in her 2 acre walled garden, built originally as part of what was Swillington Park, a large Georgian estate.

Abundant Earth is a small workers' co-operative producing fresh organic vegetables on a 1 acre garden and which are sold to the good folk of Durham through a weekly veg box scheme. It is the creation of two family couples, **Wilf Richards** and Beth Currie, along with Matt Whittaker and Jo-Anne Bolton. In addition to the garden, there is also a flock of hens kept for their eggs, sheep for meat, plenty of fruit trees, and the team make wooden bowls, willow baskets and felt fairies, and run both permaculture and craft courses. Oh, and Beth is a registered celebrant for weddings and funerals!

Philanthropy is alive and well at **Shipton Mill**. Hidden down a long unmetalled track in the heart of Gloucestershire, the mill produces a variety of speciality flours. When the present owners discovered it back in 1981, the mill had fallen into serious disrepair, but today, fully restored and functioning, it is producing stoneground flours on a commercial scale. The restoration extends to some magnificent gardens which now produce a range of vegetables along with cut and edible flowers. **Ella Hashemi** (left) and **Emily Thomas** (right) were the 2 growers employed to launch this fledgling business with the veg sold on site from the 'Harvest Table' to mill staff and customers, along with any visitors who drop by. The flowers are sold through local retailers and catering outlets. All are produced employing the biodynamic principles of Rudolf Steiner.

Hidden in woods just outside Yeovil, **Tinkers Bubble** is a small community of individual family units drawn together by a shared passion for low impact living. All buildings are rough-build wood, straw bale, or, mud cob, and all are serviced by off-grid power, water and sanitation. Whilst living space is organised by family group, social activity and food production – with its veg and fruit production, small dairy herd, sheep and chickens – along with cooking and eating facilities are communal. **Pedro** is one of the community growers whilst **Jake** was part of the team responsible for the care of the 2 working horses, **Charlie** being the one on duty when I was there.

The City of Bristol is endowed with an extensive strip of the highest quality agricultural land around its northern border. It is home to numerous small-scale producers but in 2015 the City Council backed a proposal from the West of England Transport Partnership to push a bus-way through it! *Humphrey Lloyd* is one of the growers working land right next to the proposed route. Humphrey works his 3 acres or so to produce organic vegetables and salads which are sold locally under his business name of *Edible Futures*. Despite protests the route has been developed, but there is hope for the future in all sides now seeking to work towards a new mutually respectful dialogue through which the importance of Grade 1 agricultural land is better recognised in national and local planning policy.

When I visited them, **Helen** and **Stuart Kearney** were 12 months into a four year project to develop a 5.5 acre plot of 'virgin' land at Greenham Reach on the Somerset/Devon border - named by them as **Elder Farm** - into a small farm producing saleable food crops and herbs for Helen's medicinal practice. They had moved to the site with their 2 daughters as tenants of the Ecological Land Co-operative,

a organisation set up to assist would-be farmers realise their dreams by providing access to land at affordable rents and with planning permission for experimental sustainable mixed small-holdings. All services are off grid and all production must be organic. The no dig methods of Charles Dowding come in handy in quickly creating the herb beds!

The Cross Green area of Leeds is significantly above national average in indices of deprivation and a large number of residents living alone gives rise to high rates of mental illness. **Cross Green 'Growing Together'** was launched by the community of Cross Green and local environmental charity, Hyde Park Source, as a small project to create a communal garden space on an unused bridge. A year later it had evolved into an ambitious project also to transform land alongside the railway from a derelict eyesore into a food-growing space and a provider of outdoor activity for residents. **Mary Brennan** is a resident, social entrepreneur and project volunteer who was founding treasurer for the project.

Yorkley Court was a farm of 180 acres or so on the edge of the Forest of Dean. When the last known owner died some 80 odd years ago, a self appointed 'trust' was formed to oversee the tenanting out of the land. During a break in tenancies, though, a group of environmental activists moved in to establish a community based on an alternative vision for society. The 'squatters' made rough-built dwellings, grew food, and as years passed by created **Yorkley Court Community Farm**. In response the 'trust' put the farm on the market! To cut a long and acrimonious story short, a local multi-millionaire was awarded ownership by the courts at seemingly well below market value - despite the community tracking down descendants of the last owners. The residents of YCCF were evicted and homes smashed in March 2016.

Ashley Wheeler grows on land leased at *Trill Farm*, a 300 acre organic estate set in the rolling hills and woodlands of east Devon. The estate was bought in 2008 by Romy Fraser, founder of Neil's Yard Remedies, with the aim of developing a community of small businesses that worked together using the resources of the land. Ashley, along with partner Kate and their young family, have been at Trill working the 2.5 acre garden according to traditional organic principles since 2010. They produce around 2 tonnes of salad a year with over 80 different varieties of leaves and flowers.

Things start to move at a cracking pace as spring unfurls at **St Helen's Farm** (pages 30-31) located just outside Boston Spa. This is the main planting season for most of the farm's crops and means temporary faces in the workforce - along with lots of prayers for rain! Most of the 50 or so varieties of vegetable and salad crops are sown and planted successively to maximise harvesting periods, making a complex growing schedule. Half a dozen different varieties of spouting broccoli alone are sown and then planted, for example, each with a different harvest period, in a spring extravaganza masterminded by co-owner Jonnie Watson. **Mark** was leading the planting team the day I visited.

Stroud Community Agriculture is a community-led business which produces fresh biodynamically-grown fruit, veg and meat. Members pay an annual fee plus a further payment related to the amount of produce they consume. The business is owned and controlled by the members who employ the farmers, Mark and Sam, who have access to around 30 acres of land leased from Stroud's Hawkwood College, along with 25 or so acres in the nearby village of Brookthorpe. The enterprise provides vegetables for about 290 households each week, along with beef, lamb and pork as available. American-born and raised, **Page Dykstra**, was on a 2 year Biodynamic Apprentice programme.

Writer, researcher, activist and grower, **Rebecca Laughton** – known to most as Bee – has had as much impact as anyone on the agroecology movement in the UK. Probably best known as author of the definitive text, *Surviving and Thriving on the Land*, Bee is also active in the Land Workers' Alliance both as a paid researcher and activist volunteer. Her current land base where she produces vegetables and salads is 1 acre of land leased from 2 stalwarts of the organic movement, Josephine and Arthur Pearse at **Tamarisk Organic Farm** just outside Bridport in Dorset.

I first met **Rachael Moss** on a visit to Monkton Wyld Court Farm (pages 152-153) in Dorset where she was doing some stand-in milking. At the time she lived in a 'bender' in a nearby wood, and had milking goats in an adjacent field. Soon after that she moved to the relative luxury of a small isolated caravan alongside the vine fields of **Spence Farm** in Wootton Fitzpaine. Rachael lives a simple life close to the earth, fulfilling her dreams as goat keeper, free-lance gardener, and locum milker.

Rampant.
Green.
Marouding growth.
The cultured prone
To verdant overthrow.
Your farmer needs you
The battle cry,
As migrant mistrals
Sing in tune with time,
Flying by.

Martin Campodonic was head grower at **Sims Hill Shared Harvest**, one of several initiatives which are re-establishing Bristol's historic local food supply chains. It operates on the agriculturally-rich land at Frenchay also worked by Edible Futures (page 50-51). It's a member-owned and member-led co-operatively-run business overseen by an elected board and where its members invest financially in the farm in return for a share of the harvest. Members can also pay part of their 'dues' by voluntary work. The output is a wide range of seasonal veg and salad crops.

Embercombe is a charity operating from its own retreat centre a few miles outside of Exeter. It's the inspiration one Mac McCartney and arose out of an ambition to create a *'garden to grow people'*. The programmes at Embercombe aim to inspire people to take individual action for a just, peaceful and sustainable world. The underpinning belief is that we all have something that can contribute to make a world which is more communal, more caring, more connected to nature and more fulfilling. ***Fred Groom*** is garden manager and responsible for the fruit and veg production that is integral to Embercombe's programmes and provides the daily food to residents and visitors.

Growing With Grace (pages 16-17) was established over 15 years ago when a couple of visionaries bought some 2 acres of land from a bedding plant nursery. The aim was '*a working environment that respects and nurtures all people be they employees, volunteers, customers or members of the community, and recognises the interconnectedness of the goodness within us all.*' The almost total coverage of the site with glasshouses creates its own unique challenges, not least being the summer jungle that grows up anywhere left unattended! Right in the thick of things is never-too-old volunteer, ***Catherine Morrel***, who previously had been living in Portugal before discovering Growing with Grace through the World-Wide Opportunities in Organic Farming (WWOOF) scheme.

Owen Wilson, along with younger bother and Mum and Dad, lives on the neighbouring site to Elder Farm (pages 52-53). The family moved to the plot – named by them as **Steepholding** - the year before the Kearneys moved to Elder. As at Elder Farm the land is owned and administered by the Ecological Land Co-operative. Owen and family live in an off-grid wooden house, have a paddock stocked with goats and a flock of hens, and are surrounded by a 9 acre organic market and fruit garden with 2 polytunnels. All this being set up from scratch in just 18 months! Serious commitment to a sustainable low impact way of living by Mum and Dad, Alex Wilson and Ruth O'Brien!

Each summer, for a couple of weeks at a time, the organic permaculture smallholding, **Abundant Earth** in County Durham (pages 44-45), becomes the location of a WWOOF Summer Camp for young people from across Europe - including the surrounding County Durham. Smallholding proprietors, Wilf Richards and partner, Beth Currie, and Matt Whittaker and partner, Jo-Anne Bolton, extend an open invitation to share their way of life and integrate into the resident families. In doing so, the volunteers experience both the challenges and also the rich rewards of a life lived close to the earth. **Torrin** (left) was a local lad needing a bit of space, whilst **Hollin** is Wilf and Beth's youngest.

The **Poppydale** smallholding is 20 acres of land in Gloucestershire on which is located a single-room wooden house. It is home to 2 pigs, 5 piglets, 8 Soay sheep, 12 commercial sheep, 2 working horses and numerous laying chickens and various rare breed chickens. It's also the home and workplace of **Bob** and Lyn Styles who bought it when Bob tired of his production job at the BBC and they looked for a more fulfilling lifestyle. They now work and live organically on the Poppydale land aiming at self-sufficiency with any small surplus selling from their farm gate.

Just a couple of miles from Leeds city centre, tucked away behind the houses of the Hyde Park area and alongside Leeds City Academy, lies **Bedford Fields Community Forest Garden**. The half an acre or so of land is owned by Leeds City Council but a group of inspired people negotiated the right to convert it into a forest garden for the benefit of the community. After 7 years leading the project, **Joanna Dornan** (right) shared responsibility for a short while before **Ben Lawson** (left) took the reins. Both are local activists, gardeners and foragers who continue to build on the founding ethos of this ephemeral project which boasts over 215 species of edible plants and hedging and provides a wildlife oasis and open-access foraging space almost within the city centre.

Laura Burlison is High Spen born and bred. It's old mining territory in Tyne and Wear. She did herself and family proud when she gained a place at University and came away with a degree in sociology. She then went off on the seemingly obligatory world travels and it was there that something happened - she came back not, as when she graduated, wanting to be a youth worker, but a 'grower', i.e. someone who produces wholesome food, sustainably, locally and with passion! The family horse was sectioned off to just a part of his field and **The Paddock** smallholding was born, producing free-range eggs and veg on the previous equine domain.

Ed Revill is based on the Gower Peninsula in South Wales. Operating as **Swansea Biochar** he is a modern day pioneer, testing radical ideas of soil carbon regeneration using charcoal. Ed makes his charcoal on the modified rocket stoves which he uses for cooking and heating in his off-grid home within Holt's Field community. He believes that adding the 'biochar' to the soil has umpteen benefits, but not the least being locking in carbon and so reversing climate change. Conventional organic material, he points out, ends up re-releasing carbon as carbon dioxide. The quality of Ed's vegetables speaks wonders for his ideas developed over 20 years of dedication to sustainable vegetable production.

Cross Green 'Growing Together' (pages 54-55)
is an ambitious project to transform land in the Cross
Green area of Leeds from a derelict eyesore into
a productive communal growing-space. It has
required much hard graft and commitment from
residents and the volunteers who come along through
partner, Hyde Park Source. With a little mechanical
help from Keepmoat, a construction company
contracted to carry out repairs on surrounding
houses, by mid summer the first crops are in the
newly-turned and created ground - and growing!
A small corner of Leeds is turning green. A-maizing,
this is Cross Green!

'Growing Communities' Dagenham Farm was a site of concrete and glass producing bedding plants for Dagenham parks and gardens. Five years ago, Growing Communities (pages 32-33) took over the site when it closed as a council operation with the aim of enhancing their supply of locally grown produce beyond the Patchwork Farm in Hackney.

The site now produces about 5 tonnes of veg a year. In the spring, there are leeks, spring greens, spinach and multiple salad leaves. In summer and autumn, salad and tomatoes, as well as chillies, cucumbers, squashes, beans, aubergines, courgettes, strawberries and melons. This conversion has all been overseen by head grower, *Alice Holden*.

Patch workers, growers and trainees from the **Growing Communities Patchwork Farm** (pages 32-33), from right across the borough of Hackney, come together every Tuesday evening to create and pack the salad for shop orders and the veg bags distributed through Growing Communities to about 1000 households. It's the transformation of a seemingly vast array of salad leaves into **Hackney Salad** - a sought-after, award-winning, local, organic brand - and it all comes together in the heart of the borough in the yard at Stoke Newington's Old Fire Station.

94

Riverside Market Garden was created to bring ethical sustainable and local food production to Cardiff and surrounds. On 5 acres of land at St Hilary, a village 10 miles west of the city, Riverside Market Garden is a community-owned Industrial Provident Society. ***Debbie*** is the cohesive force who administers the scheme. With the Head Grower post vacant when I visited, growing rested heavily on the shoulders of then Assistant Grower, ***Tom***. Despite such pressures, since its creation some five years ago, Riverside Market Garden has routinely provided local organic vegetables and salad through a weekly veg box scheme and farmer's markets.

Sandy Lane Farm is a small family-run farm 8 miles outside of Oxford. Here **George Bennett** grows organic vegetables, rears free-range traditional breed pigs and sheep, stables horses on livery, and hosts a produce market every Thursday in his barn. George took over the farm a few years ago from his dad, **Charles**, giving up a successful career in engineering to do so. Charles, who still works as part of the partnership, had done a similar thing some 30 odd years earlier when he inherited the farm from an uncle. Charles' wife, **Sue**, completes the line up with a keen interest in livestock welfare.

The milk at **Calf at Foot** dairy in Suffolk is from Jersey cows which are purely pasture-fed – no grain feed here, it's a place where the cows roam freely across marshland pastures. Unpasteurised, unhomogenised and unadulterated in any other way, the milk comes out of the cow and goes straight into a bottle. And, it's also entirely from cows which are allowed to keep, and feed, their own calves. Calf at Foot is one of only two dairies in the UK that practice 'calf at foot dairying', milk production with real compassion. It's the inspiration and life work of **Fiona Provan**, herds-women extraordinaire.

Feisty embers
Warm fading light.
Dog-eared days
Disguise the bounty.
Come ye thankful people come,
Seize this ancient time of plenty.

Lammas Ecovillage in Pembrokeshire is a collective of low impact smallholdings which work together to promote an environmentally sensitive way of living. The residents have come from all walks of life and have each purchased their separate plots on which they have set up their individual family homes and their businesses. These include fruit and vegetable production, livestock rearing, bee keeping, woodland and willow crafts, seed production, biomass production and organic waste treatment. As owner of the village cows – all two of them - ***Tao Wimbush*** is village dairyman. The whole village is completely off grid, and water, woodland and electricity are all managed communally, as is the large Community Hub building.

Sarah and **Ash** each run one of two geographically-separate market garden sites high in the Pennine Hills above the market towns of Todmorden and Hebden Bridge. Ash opts for a site at a mere 800 feet above sea level, and bordered by trees, so she can grow 'tender' things like salad leaves. Sarah is bold and works over 1100 feet up on the moors, 'specialising' in ground veg which the wind can't reach! They join forces in supplying the surrounding towns with local organic fruit and veg as **Sagar Lane Market Gardens**. Innovative growing is needed on both sites as they seek to build soil health using permaculture principles whilst also experimenting in response to their unique conditions.

Cae Tan Community Supported Agriculture Project operates from 2 sites, the main one being 4 acres of land owned by Gower Power Community Co-operative. The co-operative was created to enable local ownership of food, electrical power and the means of exchange. The plot is within the Gower Area of Outstanding Natural Beauty, and next to a couple of Sites of Special Scientific Interest. **Tom O'Kane** is head grower and an experienced follower of biodynamic principles. He is supported by partner, **Pascale** (centre), apprentice **Liz** (left), and volunteer, Geof, plus a host of other voluntary efforts. Launched in 2015, in its first year Cae Tan CSA produced enough vegetables to feed over 50 Gower households. The team also work with schools and colleges developing projects to raise awareness of sustainable growing.

The sign on the gate said Chagfarm/Chagford Community Farm - I was looking for **Chagfood** or **Chagford Community Market Garden**. In fact I was at the gate to two separate businesses run by two brothers-in-law which are very conveniently, but confusingly, located on adjacent land! **Ed Hamer**, with business partners Chinnie and **Yssy** (also Ed's wife), is Chagfood, the market garden business and elder of the two sibling businesses. Its 5 acres of ecologically-produced vegetables, herbs and flowers, powered only by people and horses, are located on the lower slopes of Dartmoor. It's run as a crop-share community supported enterprise with members able to off-set some of the membership costs with voluntary work in the fields.

Cultivate Oxford is a co-operative with one full-time and several part-time employees who produce organic vegetables on 10 acres of land leased from the Earth Trust just north of Oxford. In keeping with the founding ethos of 'change through practical action', Cultivate Oxford has recruited over 400 members from in and around Oxford who support the venture with time and resources. Key to the sale of the co-operative's produce is its mobile greengrocer's shop, the ***Veg Van***, which delivers produce through a weekly tour around the city. ***Doireann Lalor*** is one of the core founders.

Ourganics Evolving Systems is a market garden just outside Bridport in Dorset and from where ***Pat Bowcock*** runs a debt-free business growing salad, vegetables, fruit, herbs and flowers for the local community. Pat has been living and working there for 16 years. It was originally a pony paddock. There are now raised beds, a 27 metre polytunnel, a forest garden, and other woodland planted for future generations. To water the garden, Pat has reinstated an irrigation system which had been used in the surrounding water meadows for a hundred years utilising a system of ponds and sluice gates. All this has been designed using permaculture principles and ethics, and Pat lives on site in a self-built off-grid home (known as 'Our Shed') which is the venue for permaculture courses, visits and tours.

Jonah Maurice lives off-grid for water, power and sanitation with his partner and young family in the remote Northumberland valley of Allendale. He is smallholder, woodsman and grave digger. His 14 acre, mixed smallholding is a source of food and an income generator when there is any surplus. It also houses his horse, ***Jimmy***, a key component of his work as a woodsman where, with Jimmy, he can access areas that would be impossible for anything mechanical. In many ways Jonah's life could be described as 'on the edge' and it's perhaps therefore not too surprising to find him also as local grave digger after responding to a call from the parish council. Such work though demonstrates that Jonah is also firmly embedded in the local community.

Gerald Miles farms the 120 acres of **Caerhys** located just north of St David's on the western edge of Wales. Gerald used to be a dairy farmer, but when diminishing returns from small-scale milk production forced his son, Carwyn, to make his living away from the farm, Gerald decided to set up a Community Supported Agriculture scheme through which he offered organic vegetables to the people of St David's.

Now, that CSA, with 60 members, is sufficiently robust for Carwyn to return to manage it. With the population of St David's only around 1500, their market penetration with local organic produce is astonishing. Alongside the veg, Gerald now raises Welsh Black beef cattle and a few free-range pigs, and he and Carwyn jointly grow heritage grains, Black Supreme Oats and Emmer Wheat.

Will and Hilary Chester-Master are the managers of the family business of ***Abbey Home Farm*** just outside Cirencester. The farm covers some 1600 acres and since they took over in 1991, it has all been converted to organic production. Initially, it was sheep, dairy, beef and arable, but rather than reduce the range, Will and Hilary have introduced laying hens and pigs, a 15 acre vegetable garden, soft fruit and flower growing area, and opened a farm shop and cafe. The milk is pasteurized on site in a micro-dairy which also produces yoghurt, cream and cheeses. All butchering is also on site. A field-side conference space with residential facilities has recently been added as the jewel in the crown. Abbey Home has to be one of the outstanding success stories in the 'new age' farming scene, and employs a small army of passionate workers, two of whom, ***Jamie*** (left) and ***Ian*** (centre), I caught busy summer weeding on the vegetable plots.

Martin Wolf doesn't own a farm, he owns his own experimental field station! The 'retired' Professor of Plant Pathology who worked for 28 years at the Cambridge Plant Breeding Institute, bought the 60 acre *Wakelyns Farm* in Suffolk to explore his passionate belief in diversity as the route to secure and sustainable food production. The farm is organised into multiple arrays of 'alley cropping' whereby arable crops are planted in small plots separated by belts of mixed trees. Martin argues persuasively with data-based evidence that one protects and nurtures the other. Similarly, another notable success has been the development of mixed variety barley crops – something currently banned commercially – which Martin has demonstrated are disease resistant without need for chemical or other intervention.

Ian Tolhurst is another legend of small-scale local food production. **Tolhurst Organic Partnership**, run by Ian, his wife, Tamara, and business partner, **Lin**, is located on a 20 acre site on the Hardwick Estate just outside the village of Whitchurch-on-Thames in south Oxfordshire. It is not only certified organic but certified stockfree. Tolhurst Organic was the first farm in the world to attain the 'Stockfree Organic' symbol from the Vegan Organic Network in 2004. All the vital replenishing manure is produced on the farm as organic green manure crops. The business supplies weekly veg boxes, fruit, and bread to over 200 customers around Oxfordshire.

Worton Organic Garden is the creation of Australian-raised grower, **David Blake**, and wife, Anneke. The garden is located on a couple of acres of land just outside Oxford where they have created a space of chaotic but exquisite and enormous variety. Vegetables mingle and intersperse perennial and self-seeded flowers, whilst mixed tree plantings provide a diverse year-round backdrop. David and Anneke also work 4 acres of adjacent land where they grow field vegetables and most of their apple crop, with chickens and pigs free to range and roost in the wooded borders of the field. In the midst of all this, alongside the on-site shop, Dutch-born Anneke runs an artisan cafe, *L'Arte di Mangier Bene* – 'The Art of Eating Well!'

A Garden Organic Accredited Master Gardener is someone who has been adjudged as having sufficient knowledge of organic gardening as to be able to act as a focal point for advice and support. *Robin Baxter* is one such person and who has been appointed at *HMP Rye Hill* to run an organic training scheme for prison inmates. The prison is a high security establishment near Rugby holding 660 male adults, 20% of whom are serving life sentences. The project works in conjunction with G4S, who operate the prison, and the prison's Substance Misuse Services with funds provided by Public Health England. The scheme has around 60 prisoner participants and an evaluation by Coventry University found that there is an overwhelmingly positive connection between working in the garden and the success of participants' journeys of recovery.

Gibside Community Farm is a community enterprise using land at the National Trust-owned Gibside Estate at Rowlands Gill just outside of Newcastle. Gibside is Georgian 'grand design' on a spectacular scale, with its Palladian chapel considered an architectural masterpiece. The 20 members of the farm grow in the 1 acre walled garden and on a 10 acre out-field at nearby Burnopfield. An annual subscription entitles a share of the produce, and everyone is expected to participate in farm operations. By and large, **Mick Marston** is the unofficial farm co-ordinator. In real life he is the enthusiastic Northern Development Co-ordinator for the Federation of City Farms and Community Gardens.

The family-run farm of **Shillingford Organics** is located on the outskirts of Exeter. **Martyn Bragg's** is the second generation of the Bragg family to farm here and Martyn leads a team who grow vegetables, salads, herbs and fruit - all using methods which demonstrate a passion for accompanying wildlife and biodiversity. The produce is available through Shillingford Organics online shop, local outlets and businesses, the weekly Exeter Farmers' Market, and other local markets and farm events. The farm has been fully organic since 2000. Forty acres, including 8 polytunnels, are dedicated to vegetables and alongside this are 2 orchards and various agroforestry alley schemes with further apple and fruit trees. Several flocks of organic free-range hens supplying eggs complete the line up.

The year stump withers
Dark solstice cutting in.
Light without heat.
Life, an incarcerated form.
Long shadows. Long nights.
Long, hungry
Gap

Sonia Oliver works the walled garden of the Coleshill Estate owned by the National Trust on the Oxfordshire/Wiltshire border. Coleshill village is an archetypal English village with stone-built church and pub surrounded by a patchwork quilt of fields, woodland spinney, water meadow and the estate parkland. Sonia began with a small 2 acre farm in Wiltshire in 1995 and has gradually evolved – with input from then husband, Pete, along the way - so as to now occupy about 7 acres of the National Trust-owned land in nearby Coleshill. Sonia runs a shop and box scheme from within the garden as **Coleshill Organics**, driven by a passion to provide local people with the highest quality fresh seasonal produce.

North East Organic Growers is a small worker co-operative operating on land in the village of Bomarsund, near Bedlington, twelve miles north of Newcastle. Set up in 1995, organic vegetables and fruit are grown on the 10 acre site, with a weekly membership box scheme providing the main outlet.

Over 50 different varieties of vegetables and fruit are grown, many rarely found in shops. An orchard of apple trees inherited with the site provides an autumnal bonus. Co-operative workers, ***Phil Tyler*** (left) and ***Stuart Rintoul*** (right) were the hosts for my couple of visits.

Canalside Community Food is a Community Supported Agriculture scheme serving people in the Leamington and Warwick areas. It provides weekly shares of organic vegetables, and organic fruit when in season, to its 150 or so members. The scheme leases its 7 acres of open land at Leasowe Farm, a family-run farm adjacent to the Grand Union Canal, plus 7 large polytunnels to assist year-round production. Members are encouraged to help through a membership scheme which will exchange voluntary work for reduced membership fee. ***Will Johnson*** was the head grower, and is one of several young people around the country who have graduated through Soil Association Apprenticeships at Coleshill Organics (pages 134-135).

The UK Heritage Seed Library is maintained by **Garden Organic**, a charity dedicated to promoting organic methods amongst Britain's gardeners. The collection consists of rare landrace varieties, heirloom varieties that have been saved over many generations, and varieties that have been dropped from commercial seed catalogues. Anyone can join the library and gain access to the selection of available seeds. To maintain the collection, crops are grown on a three year rotation and harvested for seed at Garden Organic's Ryton Gardens headquarters by a small library team which included ex-teacher, **Richard Smith**. In addition, a number of members of Garden Organic act as Seed Guardians sending in seed to add to the catalogue.

When the folk of Ovingham in the Tyne valley decided that they wanted to create a more sustainable village they took direct action! Specifically they set up **GO Local Food** as a member-owned food-growing co-operative. They then acquired a lease to around 2 acres of land from a local garden centre, erected 4 polytunnels and employed 2 growers as the base for a scheme which now has some 50 odd members and over 40 varieties of vegetables grown each year. **Chris Morrison** was one of the founding members and active volunteer. **Ian** (right) and **Sean** (left), were the 2 growers. Whilst summer brings excitement of a seemingly ever more exotic cropping - challenging the general perception of north east growing conditions – maintaining fresh supplies through winter and the 'hungry gap' provides a greater challenge.

Village Farm is in Devon above the Salcombe-Kingsbridge estuary. It's a farm whose soil had been exhausted by intensive arable production. Today though best friends, **Rebecca Hosking** and Tim Green, have an ambitious programme to restore fertility. Key is 'holistic planned grazing' where livestock are moved daily from one small pocket of pasture to another. The animals not only eat the vegetation and eject organic manure, but being on fresh pasture each day, also trample much of the vegetation directly into the ground. Livestock currently means a mixed herd of sheep with another ambition being to breed a sheep to match the now-extinct traditional sheep of Devon. All this whilst practising high welfare stockmanship, turning the farm into a haven for wildlife and running a couple of pigs with the sheep!

Joanne Mudhar used her life savings to buy 12 acres of agriculturally-depleted land adjacent to the village of Rushmere St Andrew where she grew up, near Ipswich. She is now turning it into **Oak Tree Low Carbon Farm**. In the first year Joanne grew vegetables on three-quarters of an acre of heavily manured soil, and sowed clover and grass on the rest. The vegetables were soon supplemented by fruit trees and bushes, and livestock as the farm became proud owner of half a dozen rare breed pigs, a clutch of dual-purpose meat and egg chickens and 2 Red Poll heifers! Joanne's vision is of a land which is at the heart of the local community, farmed sustainably and home to a financially-viable market garden.

There was a group of half a dozen or so people in the distance working in the field as the mist lurked across the dank Devon hillsides. They were rhythmically bending, rising, chopping, bending, rising, chopping. This was **Ed Hamer** and the volunteer members of **Chagford Community Market Garden** or **Chagfood** (pages 108-109)

picking some of the last crops of the winter for the 100 or so veg boxes distributed weekly through the market garden. Offsetting some of the membership cost by volunteering on the farm means that local organic vegetables can be purchased for less than the price of the factory-farmed imported produce of the local supermarket.

Chagford Community Farm or ***Chagfarm***, sited on land adjacent to Chagfood (pages 108-109 & 148-149), was set up as a community interest company by **Sylvan Friend** and brother, Davon. Qualified carpenter and business manager respectively, Sylvan and Davon launched the UK's first community-supported goat micro-dairy. Also available is goat meat, free-range pork, woodland poultry and honey - all produced to Soil Association-certified organic standards. The inspiration came from watching how the community supported farm model worked for the veg-based Chagfood run by brother-in-law, Ed Hamer, and two partners. Customers at Chagfarm CIC pay a small membership fee and in so doing commit to buying a certain amount of produce so creating a livestock farm of, and for, the local community.

Simon Fairlie and ***Gill Barron*** are the resident farmers at ***Monkton Wyld Court*** – a large house and estate in the village of Monkton Wyld in deepest Dorset. The Court is run and maintained by a resident community who try to practice a low impact environmental way of living. Decisions are all made by consensus and the farm produces much of the food consumed by the community. Its 3 Jersey cows provide the dairy input with milking by hand and, in the winter – there being no electrical power in the milking parlour – under the seemingly ancient spell of gas light.

Lily Tucker lives with Mum and Dad at Little **Brympton Ecological Micro-Farm** (pages 14-15) just outside the village of Chiselborough in Somerset. Her home is a wooden structure, off-grid for water, power and sanitation, and set in 2 acres of land where Mum and Dad, Tasha and Patch, have been granted planning permission to continue the low impact living project of the farm after its founder, Albert Holman, had to retire through ill health. As winter darkness falls, a family friend calls in and the house is converted into a communal wicker fence-making factory using willow from the garden. In the twilight, Lily dances her own mystical, magical weave.

And so my journey ends at the place where it actually began, **Lower Hewood Farm**, home of Alexa de Ferranti - farmer, curatorial entrepreneur and arts lecturer. It was from here that I first set out to explore the world of alternative small-scale and sustainable farming. Alexa runs sheep and pigs on her 45 acres of the rolling farmland on the borders of Somerset, Devon and Dorset.

So what next for the fragile 'new age' farms and market gardens? There is undoubtedly a rich array of small-scale local food producers right across the country. They, the producers, have made a bold commitment to a low impact way of life. The decision of what next would seem to be as much yours and mine, as it is theirs? Is it not up to the rest of us now to buy their produce? To support them in a meaningful and practical way and release ourselves from enslavement to the supermarket? To get back to real food? If we did, surely we can't help but start to make a real difference to the future of our threatened world.

**Feeding Body and Soul:
The Unlikely Heroes Blog**

www.feedingbodyandsoul.com

All of the visits that I made to farmers and growers are recounted in greater depth and with more images than is possible here on the blog website launched specifically to document my travels and the people I met along the way. The site provides websites and contact details for all the places visited.

Details of other people and bodies which are mentioned in the book and which are linked to the sustainable local production of food are given below:

Biodynamics Association – Charity fostering biodynamic farming and gardening in the UK. Part of the worldwide movement inspired by Rudolf Steiner. (https://www.biodynamic.org.uk/)

Coventry University-Centre for Agroecology, Water and Resilience - Transdisciplinary research centre looking at resilient food and water systems. (http://www.coventry.ac.uk/research/areas-of-research/agroecology-water-resilience/)

Charles Dowding – Market gardener and educator who promotes the use of no till/no dig methods to grow nutritious food and to enhance soil health and reduce weeds. (http://www.charlesdowding.co.uk/)

Community Interest Companies (CIC) Association - Focal point for co-operation and development of shared objectives for the 10,000 or so CICs operating across a wide spectrum of sectors in the UK. (http://www.cicassociation.org.uk/)

Community Supported Agriculture (CSA) Network – Organisation representing community supported agriculture schemes and helping define the practices of community supported agriculture in the UK. (https://communitysupportedagriculture.org.uk/)

Co-operatives UK – Network promoting, developing and uniting the thousands of co-operatively structured businesses based in the UK, and worth more than £34b to the economy. (http://www.uk.coop/)

Earth Trust – Organisation which is about the way we feel, think and act towards the environment, promoting the belief that the best way to look after the earth is to change the way we live on it. (http://www.earthtrust.org.uk/)

Ecological Land Co-operative – Charity addressing the lack of affordable sites for ecological land-based livelihoods in England in real and prcatical ways. (http://ecologicalland.coop/)

Federation of City Farms and Community Gardens - Representative body for city farms, community gardens and similar community-led organisations in the UK. (https://farmgarden.org.uk/)

Hyde Park Source – Leeds-based charity improving individual and community health and well being by improving the local environment. (http://www.hydeparksource.org/)

Land Workers Alliance - Organisation representing UK small scale farmers, and growers campaigning for policies to support sustainable agriculture. (http://landworkersalliance.org.uk/)

Organic Farmers and Growers – UK body working with producers and processors to ensure organic products meet the highest quality and reliability standards. (http://ofgorganic.org/)

Oxford Real Farming Conference – Unique gathering each January of the UK's sustainable food and farming movements offering a mix of on-farm advice, best practice in agroecological farming, and radical discussion of the global food system. (http://www.oxfordrealfarmingconference.org/)

Permaculture Association – Charity promoting permaculture, a design process for producing systems which meet human needs whilst enhancing biodiversity, reducing impact on the planet, and creating a fairer world. (https://www.permaculture.org.uk/)

Soil Association - UK food and farming charity working to save our soils and make good ethical food an available choice for everyone. (https://www.soilassociation.org/)

UK Food Sovereignty Movement – Broad-based network of individuals campaigning for a democratic sustainable and fair food system. (http://foodsovereignty.org.uk/)

Unicorn Grocery - Manchester's co-operative grocery offering a stunning range of wholesome organic foods since opening in September 1996. (http://unicorn-grocery.coop/)

Vegan Organic (Stockfree) Network – Co-ordination body researching and promoting vegan organic methods of agriculture and horticulture. (http://veganorganic.net/)

World Wide Opportunities in Organic Farming - Movement linking volunteers with organic farmers and growers to enable cultural and educational exchange to help build a sustainable global food system. (http://wwoof.net/)

Acknowledgments

Profuse thanks are due to all the farmers and growers who welcomed me into their worlds and allowed me to poke a camera into all corners of that world. Your enthusiasm and energy is an inspiration. Particular thanks are required to Alexa de Ferranti who as then Chair of Land Worker's Alliance (LWA) welcomed me into the alternative food production world of Dorset by allowing me to stay in her 'pod' and fed me whilst I was there. Also to Ashley Wheeler with whom I made the first contact as Membership Secretary of LWA and who opened so many doors. Special mention too of Ella Hashemi who not only welcomed me to her workplace but introduced me to a whole range of biodynamic practitioners across Gloucestershire. Laura Burlison must also be similarly singled out having provided several introductions in the north east.

Specific thanks and commiserations are offered to those farmers and growers whom I visited but who didn't make an entry in the book. Your contribution in terms of my education was just as great as those who do feature.

Special thanks must also go to my daughter, Katie, who in providing encouragement and words of wisdom saw more than her fair share of images and portfolios in the process of being developed into this book . Your patience, Katie, was immeasurable! The multitude of others who have contributed with thoughts and comments range so far and wide through contacts and friends that it is impossible to be specific. Heartfelt thanks to all, though perhaps particular mention of Vic Allen at Dean Clough Mills is justified as it is to him that the title of the book must be attributed.

Finally massive thanks to Jamie Sinclair, a young book designer who worked on the creation of *Unlikely Heroes* with me and whose input far exceeded the call of duty. If you need a book designer, call Jamie (Contact jamiesinclairart@gmail.com)

Walter Lewis, January 2017

First Edition of 600 Case Bound Copies
Published in 2017 by Walter Lewis
www.feedingbodyandsoul.com

All photographs were made in 2015
All Rights Reserved

Photography and Accompanying Text by Walter Lewis © 2017
Foreword by Colin Tudge © 2017
Closing the Distance by Stephen Devlin © 2017
Design by Jamie Sinclair and Walter Lewis © 2017

ISBN 978-1-78808-642-4

Printed in the United Kingdom by Henry Ling Limited, at the Dorset Press, Dorchester, DT1 1HD

To Brenda

- a much loved and missed wife, mum, and granny, whose love and support enabled so much

no fuss, just love